Usborne Engl

Level 2

Pinocchio

Retold by Mairi Mackinnon

Illustrated by Pablo Pino

English language consultant: Peter Viney

Contents

You can listen to the story online here:
www.usborneenglishreaders.com/
pinocchio

Old Geppetto was looking at his table. "I must fix that broken leg," he said. He took a piece of wood and started to carve it.

"Ouch!" said the wood. Geppetto was so surprised that he dropped it. "Shhh!" he said. "I don't want a talking table."

"Please, don't make me into a table," the wood answered. "I don't want to be a table. I want to be a boy."

"I can't make a boy," said Geppetto, "but I can make a puppet."

He carved the head, the body, the arms and legs. Then he put the puppet on the ground. "You need a name," said Geppetto. "I name you… Pinocchio!"

Pinocchio started to walk, slowly at first.
Then he started jumping around the room.
Finally, he ran into the street.

"Stop!" shouted Geppetto, and he
ran after Pinocchio.

"Why is that puppet running away?"
people asked. "Did Geppetto hurt him?
Quick, call the police!"

So the police took Geppetto away with
them, but Pinocchio just laughed and
ran home.

Pinocchio heard a noise: cri-cri-cri…
"What's that?"
"Pinocchio, Pinocchio, I am the talking cricket. I am a hundred years old. I can see that you are a silly puppet, and you will never be a good son to Geppetto. Good boys listen to their fathers. Bad, lazy boys become donkeys."

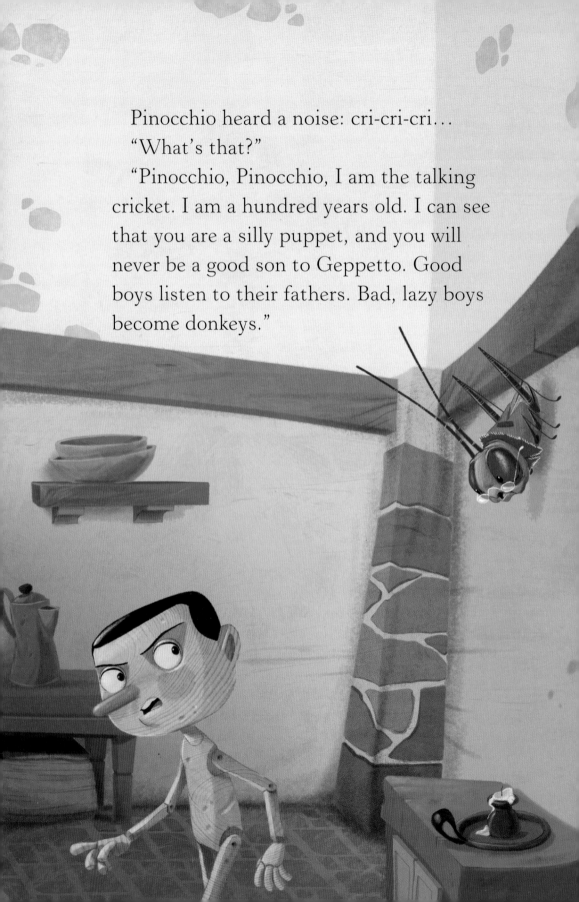

"Be quiet!" shouted Pinocchio, and he threw a piece of wood at the wall. Maybe he didn't plan to kill the cricket, but he didn't hear anything more.

It was a cold day, so he pulled a chair near to the fire. Soon he was asleep.

When he woke up, he smelled burning. "My feet! I've burned my feet!"

"Pinocchio, I'm home. Are you there?"
called Geppetto. When Pinocchio didn't
come to the door, Geppetto climbed
through the window. "Oh, my poor boy,"
he said. "I will fix your feet, but you must
promise that you will never run away again."

"Thank you, Father," said Pinocchio.
"I promise."

Geppetto made new feet. Then he made
some clothes out of paper, and some shoes.
"Tomorrow you must go to school."

"Do I have to?" asked Pinocchio.

"All good boys go to school," said Geppetto. "Now, I need to buy you a schoolbook."

Poor Geppetto had no money for a schoolbook, so he had to sell his coat. He brought the book home.

"Ooh, it doesn't look very interesting," said Pinocchio.

The next morning, Pinocchio was walking to school when he saw a crowd around a red and yellow tent.

"Are you coming to the puppet show?" asked a man. "Where's your money?"

"I don't have any," said Pinocchio. "Do you want to buy my coat?"

"Who needs a paper coat? Sell me your schoolbook instead."

Pinocchio went into the tent. Suddenly the puppets called to him. "Pinocchio, brother puppet!" He jumped on to the stage. All the puppets started dancing around him, but the crowd wasn't happy.

"Boo!" they shouted. "Go on with the show!"

"What's this?" It was the Showman. "Go back to work, all of you. And you," he said to Pinocchio, "come here. I need some wood for the fire, to cook my dinner."

"Oh, please don't burn me. My father will be so sad. He sold his only coat to buy me a schoolbook, but I sold the schoolbook to come to the show."

"Atchoo!" When the Showman felt sorry for someone, he sneezed.

"Atchoo! That's a good father. Here, take these gold coins and go back to him."

"Oh, thank you!" said Pinocchio.

On the road, Pinocchio saw a fox and a cat. They were moving very slowly. The fox had a stick, and the cat was helping him to walk. The cat had dark glasses, and the fox was showing her the way.

"Ah, Pinocchio," said the fox. "Are you going back to your poor father?"

"Soon he won't be poor," said Pinocchio. "Look, I have five gold coins."

When he said that, the cat opened her eyes wide and the fox jumped up, but Pinocchio didn't see.

"Only five?" said the fox. "Do you want five hundred? Put them in the ground in the Field of Dreams. They'll grow into money trees, and you'll be rich. Come with us. We're going there tomorrow."

They stopped at an inn and had dinner. The fox and the cat ate very well, but Pinocchio was thinking about the money trees and he wasn't hungry.

The next morning he woke up early, and paid the innkeeper.

"The fox and the cat have gone already," the innkeeper said. "They went that way. You'll soon catch them."

Pinocchio walked fast. Suddenly two robbers jumped out of the forest. They were wearing black coats, and Pinocchio couldn't see their faces. Quickly, he put the coins in his mouth.

"Give us your money, or we'll kill you!"
said the robbers. They tried to open his
mouth, but they couldn't. They tried to hurt
Pinocchio, but his hard wooden body broke
their knives. "Well, then, we'll hang you
from a tree," they said. "When you're dead,
we'll take your money."

Poor Pinocchio! The robbers pulled a rope
around his neck, and the coins fell out of his
mouth. Then everything went dark.

When Pinocchio woke up, he was lying in bed in a comfortable bedroom. A beautiful fairy was smiling at him. She had blue hair and a blue dress. "I'm so glad that you're better," she said. "Now you can go back to your father."

"I don't have a father," said Pinocchio. His nose started growing. "I mean, I do have a father! I'm a good son." His nose grew some more. "I'm a bad son, but I'm going to school. I like school." Now his nose was touching the window!

The fairy laughed. "Oh, Pinocchio, you must tell the truth, or your nose will grow and grow." She opened the window. "Birds, come and help me." All kinds of birds came and pecked Pinocchio's nose until it was short again.

One of them spoke to the blue fairy. "Pinocchio," the fairy said, "your father is so worried about you. He has gone to sea to try and find you. We'll send the birds to him. They can tell him that you are safe with me. But you must start going to school."

The next morning, the fairy gave Pinocchio some new clothes and a schoolbook. Pinocchio was a good student, and he soon had lots of friends. Not all of his friends were good students.

"Forget school," they said one morning. "Today we are going to Playland."

"What's Playland?" asked Pinocchio.

"It's the best country in the world!" said his friends. "It's full of toys and games and cake and chocolate. There is no school, and you can have fun all day."

"Really?" said Pinocchio. Just then they saw twenty-four donkeys pulling a coach. Instead of horseshoes, they were wearing white boots. The coach was almost full of boys. All Pinocchio's friends jumped in.

"Sorry," said the coachman. "There's no space for you."

"I'll ride on one of the donkeys," said Pinocchio. He jumped up.

"Silly boy," said a sad voice. "Run away, before it's too late. A donkey's life is no fun."

"Wait," said Pinocchio. "My donkey is crying!"

"We can't stop," said the coachman. "Anyway, donkeys don't cry, you know."

Soon they arrived in Playland. It really was a magic place. Pinocchio and his friends had fun from morning until night.

One morning, Pinocchio's head felt strange. He touched his ears, then looked in a mirror. He had donkey's ears! He fell on his hands and knees, and he couldn't get up.

Then he remembered the old cricket. "Oh," he cried. "I am a stupid puppet and a bad son. Dear father, dear blue fairy, what have I done?"

"Come out!" shouted the coachman. "Now that you're a donkey, you have to work. No, you are too lazy to work. I'll throw you into the sea."

"Please, no!" cried Pinocchio, but the coachman didn't listen. He put a rope around Pinocchio's legs, and threw him into the water.

Suddenly Pinocchio saw a bright blue
light. "The blue fairy!" he thought. Lots of
little fish swam around him. The rope was
gone, and he was a puppet again. Quickly he
swam towards the light…

…and again everything went dark.

"What happened? Where am I?"
Pinocchio shouted. Then he saw another
light, a little yellow one. He walked nearer
until he could see it better. It was a candle
on a table, and sitting at the table was…

"Father!" shouted Pinocchio. "Is it
really you?"

"Oh, my dear boy," said Geppetto,
and he put his arms around him.

"But how can you be here?"

"I was looking for you, Pinocchio. I went to sea in a small boat, but there was a terrible storm. An enormous shark ate my boat, and I have been here since then. I had some food and candles, but they're almost finished now."

"Then we must get out, Father. Come with me, and we'll swim back to land. I'll help you. I'm very good at swimming."

Pinocchio took Geppetto's hand, and found the way to the shark's mouth. Luckily, the shark was sleeping with its mouth open. It didn't even wake up when Pinocchio and Geppetto jumped out.

Pinocchio swam and swam, and at last they reached the land. Soon they found a road. Beside the road were two hungry animals.

"Pinocchio, help me, I can't walk!" cried the fox.

"Pinocchio, help me, I can't see!" cried the cat. "It wasn't true before, but now it is."

"Well, then, you'll never play tricks on poor puppets again," said Pinocchio.

Soon after, they saw a little white house between the trees. "There must be someone at home," said Pinocchio. He went to the door.

"Come in," said a little voice. Pinocchio looked up and saw a cricket. "Dear Mr. Cricket, whose house is this?"

"It's mine," said the cricket. "Am I your dear cricket now? Last time I saw you, you threw a piece of wood at me."

"Oh, wise cricket, I'm so sorry!" said Pinocchio. "I promise I'll never hurt you again. Now I just want to be a good boy and help my poor father."

"And you'll go to school?"

"Yes!"

"And you'll work hard?"

"Yes! Yes!"

Pinocchio remembered his promise. Every day he went to school, and after school he worked. One night, he had a dream.

"Pinocchio, Pinocchio," said the blue fairy. "I can see that you've changed. From tomorrow, everything will be different."

Pinocchio woke up. The sun was shining brightly. He touched his face. It was soft and warm. His body was warm, too. He jumped out of bed, and looked in the mirror.

"Father, come and see! I'm a boy! I'm a real boy at last!"

About the story

Carlo Collodi was an Italian writer. He lived in Florence. He wrote *The Adventures of Pinocchio* in 1881 for a children's newspaper. Stories just for children were new in Italy, and Collodi's story was very popular.

When Collodi first wrote about Pinocchio, he ended the story when the fox and the cat hang Pinocchio from a tree. The head of the newspaper thought that this was too sad for his readers, so Collodi wrote a new ending, where Pinocchio turns into a real boy at last.

This is what Pinocchio looked like in the first book. Now you can find him in movies, plays, books and pictures, and people still say that your nose will grow longer if you don't tell the truth...

Bad puppet!

Choose a word to finish each sentence.

1.

Pinocchio .... away
from home.

ran   laughed   smelled

2.

Pinocchio ....
his schoolbook.

opened   sold   dropped

3.

Pinocchio .... a piece of
wood at Mr Cricket.

shouted   threw   carved

4.

Pinocchio .... to Playland
instead of school.

talked   started   went

Mixed-up story

Can you put these pictures and sentences in order?

A.

"You'll go to school and work hard?" said Mr. Cricket.

B.

Pinocchio was a real boy at last.

C.

Sitting at the table was Geppetto!

D.

"Are you coming to the puppet show?" asked a man.

E.
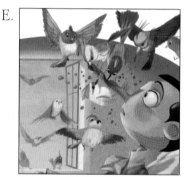
The birds came and pecked Pinocchio's nose.

F.
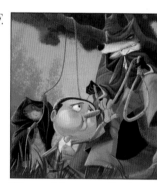
The robbers pulled a ro around Pinocchio's nec

G.

Pinocchio had donkey's ears!

H.

"Forget school," said Pinocchio's friends. "We are going to Playland."

I.

"I name you... Pinocch said Geppetto.

Is that true?

Choose a sentence for each picture.

1.

Bad, lazy boys become donkeys.

A. Mr. Cricket says Pinocchio will never be a good son.

B. Mr. Cricket says Geppetto will never be a good father.

2.

Your gold coins will grow into money trees.

A. Pinocchio thinks the fox and the cat are telling the truth.

B. Pinocchio thinks the fox and the cat are telling lies.

3.

I don't have a father.

A. Pinocchio's nose grows longer when he forgets things.

B. Pinocchio's nose grows longer when he tells lies.

4.

I'll throw you into the sea.

A. The Coachman says Pinocchio is too lazy to work.

B. The Coachman is too lazy to throw Pinocchio into the sea.

People and animals

Match the people and animals to the sentences below.

1. The fox and the cat

2. The birds

3. Geppetto

4. The Showman

5. Mr. Cricket

6. The Blue Fairy

A.	B.
He tells Pinocchio that bad boys become donkeys.	He sold his coat to buy a schoolbook.
C.	D.
He sneezes when he feels sorry for someone.	They peck Pinocchio's nose.
E.	F.
She can see that Pinocchio has changed.	They try to steal Pinocchio's money.

Where did Pinocchio...

Choose the places that answer the questions below.

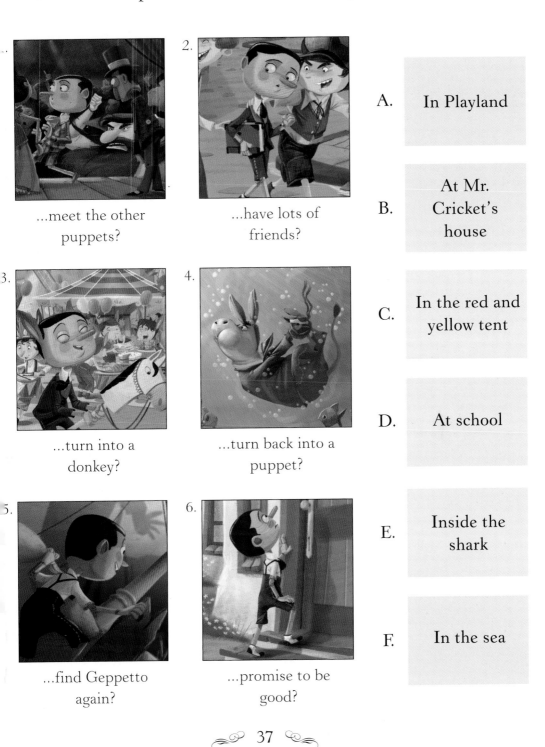

...meet the other puppets?

2. ...have lots of friends?

3. ...turn into a donkey?

4. ...turn back into a puppet?

5. ...find Geppetto again?

6. ...promise to be good?

A.   In Playland

B.   At Mr. Cricket's house

C.   In the red and yellow tent

D.   At school

E.   Inside the shark

F.   In the sea

Word list

atchoo! (excl) the noise you make when you sneeze.

candle (n) a wax stick that you burn to give light. Before there was electric light, people used candles.

carve (v) to cut wood or stone into a shape.

coach (n) something that you ride in, usually pulled by horses.

coin (n) a piece of money, made of metal.

cricket (n) a type of insect that makes a noise by rubbing its legs together.

crowd (n) lots of people together.

donkey (n) an animal like a horse, but smaller, with long ears.

glad (adj) pleased and happy.

glasses (n pl) normally you wear glasses to help you see better. Blind people sometimes wear dark glasses.

fix (v) if something is broken or doesn't work, you fix it.

hang (v) to hold something up with string or rope so that it doesn't touch the ground. This can be a way to kill a person.

inn (n) a place where you can pay for a meal or to stay for the night.

innkeeper (n) the person who works in an inn and makes sure that everyone gets what they want.

knee (n) the part that bends in the middle of your leg.

peck (v) when a bird pecks something, it uses its beak (its mouth) to make a hole in it or eat it.

play tricks (v) when you play tricks on someone, you make them believe something that isn't true.

promise (v) when you promise something, you say something and then make sure it happens.

puppet (n) a toy that looks like a person. You can make its head and body move.

reach (v) to arrive at a place.

robber (n) someone who steals things.

rope (n) something that you use to tie things together, or to tie around things so that you can pull them.

run away (v) to escape from a person or a place.

shark (n) a type of sea fish. Sharks can be very large, and often have sharp teeth.

show (n) something that you go to see for fun. A show can have acting, dancing, music or pictures, and normally you have to pay for a ticket.

silly (adj) not intelligent or serious.

sneeze (v) when you sneeze, air comes out of your mouth suddenly and with a loud noise.

stage (n) when you go to a show, the stage is where the actors or dancers are.

stick (n) a thin piece of wood. People sometimes use a stick to help them stand or walk.

tell the truth (v) if you tell the truth, what you say is true.

tent (n) a tent is made of cloth and sometimes looks like a small house. It can be used for camping or for shows.

Answers

Bad puppet!
1. ran
2. sold
3. threw
4. went

Mixed-up story
I, D, F, E, H,
G, C, A, B

What's true?
1. A
2. A
3. B
4. A

People and animals
1. F
2. D
3. B
4. C
5. A
6. E

Where did Pinocchio...
1. C
2. D
3. A
4. F
5. E
6. B

You can find information about other
Usborne English Readers here:
www.usborneenglishreaders.com

Designed by Hope Reynolds

Series designer: Laura Nelson

Edited by Jane Chisholm

With thanks to Rosie Hore

Digital imaging by Nick Wakeford

Page 32: Portrait of Carlo Collodi (engraving) © De Agostini picture library/Bridgeman images
Pinocchio illustration © The British Library Board/Scala, Florence

First published in 2017 by Usborne Publishing Ltd.,
Usborne House, 83-85 Saffron Hill, London EC1N 8RT, England.
www.usborne.com Copyright © 2017 Usborne Publishing Ltd.